THE ULTIMATE B'NAI MITZVAH HANDBOOK

A Planning Guide & Workbook

Written by:
Mildred Brill Schorr

Published by: Mitzvah Memories, LLC

ISBN 0-9765539-0-2

This book is dedicated to:

_____

With love from: _____

On this special day _____

B'nai Mitzvah Memories

There are moments in our lives and the lives of those we love that define who we are and who we hope to become. We acknowledge, honor and celebrate birth, marriage, anniversaries and our culture's history as milestones during our life's journey. You and your family are about to embark on the planning of one of the most precious of these moments...your child's Bar or Bat Mitzvah. Mazel Tov!

Jews historically celebrate the coming of adolescence as a joyful, significant step in their child's development. In addition to being the ceremonial occasion that marks the time when a young person is recognized as an adult in the Jewish community, it is also an opportunity for families to reunite and spend time together.

It is an opportunity for you to create meaningful memories that last a lifetime.

Though this celebration is a time of great happiness, it can also be a time of increased stress, and it is important that the joy and meaning of this special occasion not be lost in the numerous details of planning such a major event.

This workbook was written to help you simpify the planning of your child's Bar or Bat Mitzvah. By using these guidelines, you and your family can move forward knowing that all the details that go into creating a successful party and a memorable occasion will be addressed. Most of the major decisions should be made well in advance of the event. If unexpected roadblocks arise there will be enough time to adjust your plans. No matter how organized you are, leave room for the unexpected.

- Expect the unexpected -

If plans don't work out exactly to your expectations, just remember... your guests don't know what your expectations were!

How you choose to celebrate this milestone in your child's life depends on many factors, including your background, religious denomination, economic situation, location, and family dynamics.
B'nai Mitzvah celebrations can range from a simple kiddush after the service, to a multi-day celebration; from a special event for a few select friends to a trip (perhaps to Israel) for just the family. Some will have a traditional feel, while others might be more contemporary.
Only you and your family can decide what will make this a memorable and meaningful event.

As you plan this celebration remember why you are doing this and for whom!
Take time to enjoy and recognize the moments of growth and the accomplishments of your child.

B'nai Mitzvah Memories

The following is a sampling of possible B'nai Mitzvah celebrations.

**A simple kiddush or luncheon at the synagogue immediately
following the service.**

A party for the friends of the B'nai Mitzvah.
An afternoon or evening party just for the friends of the B'nai Mitzvah. This can take
many forms, you are only limited by your imagination and your pocketbook!

A reception following the service or an evening reception.
A celebration with all the guests, young and old alike,
at the temple or at a different location.

Using This Manual

This workbook enables you to record and organize, choose what is relevant for your situation and bypass the rest. Each page addresses a possible situation that you may encounter while planning.

As you start to use this workbook you will notice it is color coded to enable quick manuevering from one subject to the next. The first few pages provide projected budget, tips and a timeline. There are some very simple ways to economize without compromising the quality or outcome of the event. Refer back to the tips pages from time to time, as you move along in the planning process.

Because we live in a time when many families have relatives scattered around the globe it is challenging to gather the whole family in one location. For some families this may be a time to encourage a family reunion. This gives the children an opportunity to see themselves within the context of their extended family. If your family and friends need to travel a great distance it is helpful to plan accordingly. You can help make their trip as comfortable as possible, by arranging hotels, as well as providing information about local amenities that would make their stay more enjoyable. Therefore this workbook contains pages devoted to the needs of your out of town guests as well as planning auxilary events, such as a Friday night dinner or a Sunday brunch.

This book is meant to be used. Write, scribble and doodle.

keep in mind...
Planning a successful party is a creative process and as with any creative
endeavor, each seed planted grows and expands exponentially.
By giving yourself the time to develop these ideas,
the process can be joyful, and the
results a gift to your child.

E
V
E
N
T
S

V
E
N
D
O
R
S

G
U
E
S
T
S

T I M E L I N E

*The following timeline offers suggestions
as to when certain
tasks should be accomplished.
Use these guidelines to fit your individual needs.
There may be specific considerations that would impact
your celebration and the timing of preparations. One
such consideration might be the time of year. June
is typically wedding season therefore space at a hotel
ballroom might be in high demand. In such a case
reserving a reception site more than
15 months prior to the event date might be in order.*

9-15 MONTHS

Calculate number of anticipated guests	50-51

Consider options for theme and style of party

Budget for money and time	11
Research reception sites	34-35

6-12 MONTHS

Hire entertainment	28-29
Hire florist	31
Hire caterer	26
Hire photographer	22-33
Hire videographer	38
Reserve out of town guest accomodations	45

4-6 MONTHS

Order invitations and thank you notes	41-43
Order party favors	30
Order decorations	27
Order yarmulkas, tallit	15
Compile guest list	52-103
Shop for family clothing	11

2-4 MONTHS

Organize Welcome gifts	45
Plan Friday oneg, Saturday kiddush	19-20
Sunday brunch	22
Address and mail invitations	52-103

1-2 MONTHS

Gather maps and local information	46
Hire transportation	46
Set hair appointments, shop for clothing	
Order cake	25

1-4 WEEKS

Assign synagogue service honors	15
Assign candle lighting honors	44
Finalize head count for caterer	104-109
Create seating and placement cards	47-49
Order challah	25
Decide songs for dj	28-29

In the Beginning

To begin planning, consider how much you are willing and able to spend. After compiling estimates, it may be necessary to establish priorities in order to remain close to your projected budget. Remember to plan for the unexpected, incidental expenses that inevitably occur.

Once you have a budget in mind, it is time to start organizing your reception. The next few pages of this handbook include tips and ideas that can save you time and money.

PLANNING TIME

- Refer to the timeline on pages 6-7 of the handbook to help you prioritize and map out a plan. The timeline is color coded for easy reference.
- How much time can you devote to planning? It may be more efficient to hire an event planner. Usually an event planner will help with specific tasks, as many or few as need be.
- If there is another child becoming a bar/bat mitzvah during the same service; you will be sharing this special day with another family. Start out on the right foot by meeting the family early in the planning process. It is important to understand the expectations each family may have and determine which costs may be shared.

CHOOSING A RECEPTION SITE

- Determine the approximate number of guests before choosing a site.
- Consider the atmosphere you want to create. Will it be formal or informal? Do you want a "kids only" party or a reception for family and friends of all ages?
- Do you want the reception in your home?
- How far from your home or synagogue do you want to travel? Are your guests able to travel from place to place, or are there reasons to keep activities confined to one venue?
- Do you need a venue that is wheelchair accessible?
- If possible choose a site with a foyer or suitable space separate from the main event for anyone who may need to retreat from the festivities.
- Consider the season, in summer a room that opens to a view or has an outside patio may be desirable whereas in winter when the sun sets early a room with a view may be inconsequential.
- Is there a kosher caterer on site or one that can be used?
- Do you want a site that is all inclusive, or a site where you choose all the vendors separately?

RECEPTION DETAILS

- Consider setting up a theme or style for your event. Choosing color schemes, decorations, favors, centerpieces and entertainment may all be easier if based around a single theme.
- Consider a candlelighting ceremony to honor special guests.
- Compile photos of memorable events from your child's life and create a short video or DVD to show at the reception.
- Create a sign-in board or memory book for guests to sign as they enter the reception site.
- Be considerate of the different age groups present. Vary the type of music and minimize the sound level during the meal.

BUDGETING TIPS

- Create your own centerpieces and decorations.
- Create your own invitations.
- To save on postage use standard size envelops.
- RSVP by phone or email.
- Bake desserts in advance and freeze for Friday night kiddish.
- Ask friends to bake, or organize a "baking party".
- Shop and compare prices on the internet.
- Order food and bakery platters from the supermarket or discount food warehouse.
- Get an accurate head count, don't order extra meals.
- Buy your own alcoholic beverages when possible.
- Add tax and gratuity when estimating your expenses.
- Leave the smallest deposit possible on your credit card.

**When negotiating contracts, pay attention to every detail.
If in doubt, ask questions.**

**Imagine it's 11:00 PM, the last guest has left, you are exhilarated and exhausted...
At that moment you discover your caterer has left the building!
Now you are responsible for cleaning up,
folding the tables and stacking the chairs.
Probably not the ideal scenario to end an otherwise perfect evening.
But...with a little forethought this will not happen to you!**

MISCELLANEOUS IDEAS AND TIPS

SAVE THE DATE POSTCARD/LETTER/EMAIL

- Send "Save the Date" cards approximately six months ahead, thereby giving out of town guests ample time to make travel arrangements.

INVITATIONS

- It is more cost effective to order 10-20 extra invitations than to add a second order if you run short. By doing so you allow for mistakes and additional guests that you may add to your list.
- Be sure to check and check again that all information is correct before printing.
- Any non standard size envelope will be an additional postage charge.

CATERER

- Before finalizing your menu, request a food tasting.
- Clarify who is responsible for rental items, i.e. tables, linens, tableware. You may save money by renting directly from the supplier, but you become liable, for damages and breakage.
- Ask what is included in the quoted price, so as not to be surprised by extra charges.

PHOTOGRAPHER/VIDEOGRAPHER

- Give the photographer a list of significant people and specific events (i.e. candlelighting ceremony) to capture during the reception. Give this same list to a person that can be a reference point for the photographer.
- Ask who will own the negatives.

OUT OF TOWN GUESTS

- Ask for a group rate when reserving guest rooms. Most hotels will offer a discount for ten or more rooms.
- Print maps to and from all destinations, include a phone number where you can be contacted if need be.

TABLE SEATING

- In order to work out the seating arrangements, write each name on a post-it note. Draw circles on poster board for the number of tables needed. Then move people around until you are sure Aunt June and Aunt Rose, who haven't talked to each other for the last 20 years, aren't sitting at the same table!

EXTRAS

- If you plan any home improvements, do them well in advance of the scheduled bar/bat mitzvah date.

	PROJECTED COST	ACTUAL COST
FRIDAY		
- Dinner		
- Oneg		
SATURDAY		
- Kiddush/Luncheon		
- Reception		
- Bakery		
- Caterer		
- Decorations		
- Entertainment		
- Favor		
- Florist		
- Photographer		
- Videographer		
SUNDAY		
- Brunch		
MISCELLANEOUS		
- Clothing		
- Invitations		
- Transportation		

EVENTS

Ceremony

Friday dinner

Friday oneg

Saturday kiddush

Saturday luncheon

Reception

Sunday brunch

EVENTS

Ceremony

Friday dinner

Friday oneg

Saturday kiddush

Saturday luncheon

Reception

Sunday brunch

Synagogue

Address

Phone

Email

Fax

Contacts

Rabbi

Cantor

ITEMS TO BRING TO SYNAGOGUE

Friday

Saturday

TALLIT/YARMULKAS

Company

Address

Phone

Email

Fax

Cost

Although this book is dedicated to planning the Bar/Bat Mitzvah parties, there are a few specific parts of the service that you will need to prepare in advance.

You will be given the opportunity to call one or more honored guests to the bimah for an aliyah. If you would like to include more family or friends in the service, discuss with your rabbi how this can be accomplished.

PARENTS' SPEECH

You may be given the opportunity to say a few words to your child while on the bimah. Prepare in advance what you will say. Whether it be a quote, a poem or an original speech, try to keep it concise, heartfelt and memorable.

ALIYOT AND OTHER HONORS

Company	
Contact name	
Phone	
Address	
Email	
Fax	

DETAILS OF ESTIMATE

Capacity	
Cost	
Included	
Not included	
Restrictions	
Additional information	
Date of contract	
Total cost	
Deposit	
Balance due	

MENU

ITEM	COST

	MENU	
	ITEM	COST

Company

Contact name

Phone

Address

Email

Fax

DETAILS OF ESTIMATE

Capacity

Cost

  Included

  Not included

  Restrictions

Additional information

Date of contract

Total cost

Deposit

Balance due

Company	
Contact name	
Phone	
Address	
Email	
Fax	

DETAILS OF ESTIMATE

Capacity	
Cost	
Included	
Not included	
Restrictions	
Additional information	
Date of contract	
Total cost	
Deposit	
Balance due	

MENU

ITEM	COST

Company	
Contact name	
Phone	
Address	
Email	
Fax	

DETAILS OF ESTIMATE

Capacity	
Cost	
Included	
Not included	
Restrictions	
Additional information	
Date of contract	
Total cost	
Deposit	
Balance due	

MENU

ITEM	COST

Company	
Contact name	
Phone	
Address	
Email	
Fax	

DETAILS OF ESTIMATE

Capacity	
Cost	
Included	
Not included	
Restrictions	
Additional information	
Date of contract	
Total cost	
Deposit	
Balance due	

MENU

ITEM	COST

VENDORS

Bakery

Caterer

Decorations

Entertainment

Favors

Florist

Photography

Reception sites

Rental supplies

Videography

VENDORS

Bakery

Caterer

Decorations

Entertainment

Favors

Florist

Photography

Reception sites

Rental supplies

Videography

Company	
Contact name	
Phone	
Address	
Email	
Fax	

ITEM	COST

Company	
Contact name	
Phone	
Address	
Email	
Fax	

ITEM	COST

Company	
Contact name	
Phone	
Address	
Email	
Fax	

ITEM	COST

Company	
Contact name	
Phone	
Address	
Email	
Fax	

ITEM	COST

Company	
Contact name	
Phone	
Address	
Email	
Fax	

ITEM	COST

Company	
Contact name	
Phone	
Address	
Email	
Fax	

ITEM	COST

Company	
Contact name	
Phone	
Address	
Email	
Fax	

ITEM	COST

Company	
Contact name	
Phone	
Address	
Email	
Fax	

ITEM	COST

Company	
Contact name	
Phone	
Address	
Email	
Fax	

ITEM	COST

Company	
Contact name	
Phone	
Address	
Email	
Fax	

ITEM	COST

Company	
Contact name	
Phone	
Address	
Email	
Fax	

ITEM	COST

Company	
Contact name	
Phone	
Address	
Email	
Fax	

ITEM	COST

Company	Company
Contact name	Contact name
Phone	Phone
Address	Address
Email	Email
Fax	Fax
DETAILS OF ESTIMATE	**DETAILS OF ESTIMATE**
Date of deposit	Date of deposit
Deposit amount	Deposit amount
Balance due	Balance due

Company	Company
Contact name	Contact name
Phone	Phone
Address	Address
Email	Email
Fax	Fax
DETAILS OF ESTIMATE	**DETAILS OF ESTIMATE**
Date of deposit	Date of deposit
Deposit amount	Deposit amount
Balance due	Balance due

IDEAS AND INSTRUCTIONS FOR DJ OR OTHER ENTERTAINER	SONG LIST

Company	
Contact name	
Phone	
Address	
Email	
Fax	

ITEM	COST

Company	
Contact name	
Phone	
Address	
Email	
Fax	

ITEM	COST

Company	
Contact name	
Phone	
Address	
Email	
Fax	

ITEM	COST

Company	
Contact name	
Phone	
Address	
Email	
Fax	

ITEM	COST

Company
Contact name
Phone
Address
Email
Fax

ITEM	COST

Company
Contact name
Phone
Address
Email
Fax

ITEM	COST

Company
Contact name
Phone
Address
Email
Fax

ITEM	COST

Company
Contact name
Phone
Address
Email
Fax

ITEM	COST

Company	Company
Contact name	Contact name
Phone	Phone
Address	Address
Email	Email
Fax	Fax
DETAILS OF ESTIMATE	DETAILS OF ESTIMATE
Date of deposit	Date of deposit
Deposit amount	Deposit amount
Balance due	Balance due

Company	Company
Contact name	Contact name
Phone	Phone
Address	Address
Email	Email
Fax	Fax
DETAILS OF ESTIMATE	DETAILS OF ESTIMATE
Date of deposit	Date of deposit
Deposit amount	Deposit amount
Balance due	Balance due

IDEAS AND INSTRUCTIONS FOR PHOTOGRAPHER

SIGNIFICANT PEOPLE MOMENTS TO CAPTURE

Company		
Contact name		
Phone		
Address		
Email		
Fax		

DETAILS OF ESTIMATE

Capacity
Cost
Included
Not included
Restrictions
Additional information
Date of contract
Total cost
Deposit
Balance due

MENU	
ITEM	COST

Company		
Contact name		
Phone		

Address		

Email		
Fax		

DETAILS OF ESTIMATE

Capacity	
Cost	
Included	
Not included	
Restrictions	
Additional information	
Date of contract	
Total cost	
Deposit	
Balance due	

MENU

ITEM	COST

Company	
Contact name	
Phone	
Address	
Email	
Fax	

ITEM	COST

Company	
Contact name	
Phone	
Address	
Email	
Fax	

ITEM	COST

Company	
Contact name	
Phone	
Address	
Email	
Fax	

ITEM	COST

Company	
Contact name	
Phone	
Address	
Email	
Fax	

ITEM	COST

Company

Contact name

Phone

Address

Email

Fax

DETAILS OF ESTIMATE

Date of deposit

Deposit amount

Balance due

Company

Contact name

Phone

Address

Email

Fax

DETAILS OF ESTIMATE

Date of deposit

Deposit amount

Balance due

Company

Contact name

Phone

Address

Email

Fax

DETAILS OF ESTIMATE

Date of deposit

Deposit amount

Balance due

Company

Contact name

Phone

Address

Email

Fax

DETAILS OF ESTIMATE

Date of deposit

Deposit amount

Balance due

GUEST INFORMATION

Invitations and save the date cards

Sample text and salutations

Letter to non jewish friends

Candlelighting

Synagogue-Aliyot and other honors

Out of town guest considerations

Table seating

Tentative guest list

Alphabetical guest pages

Master guest list

GUEST INFORMATION

Invitations and save the date cards

Sample text and salutations

Letter to non jewish friends

Candlelighting

Synagogue-Aliyot and other honors

Out of town guest considerations

Table seating

Tentative guest list

Alphabetical guest pages

Master guest list

Company

Contact name

Phone

Address

Email

Fax

Style

#_____invitations $_____

#_____envelopes $_____

#_____response cards $_____

#_____thank you cards $_____

total $_____

Company

Contact name

Phone

Address

Email

Fax

Style

#_____invitations $_____

#_____envelopes $_____

#_____response cards $_____

#_____thank you cards $_____

total $_____

JAY'S
BAR MITZVAH

SAVE THE DATE
OCTOBER 10, 2010

INVITATION TO FOLLOW

Company

Contact name

Phone

Address

Email

Fax

Style

#_____notecards $_____

#_____envelopes $_____

#_____postcards $_____

total $_____

It is with great pleasure that my family and I
invite you to join in our celebration
when I will be called to the Torah as a Bat Mitzvah
Saturday, June second, two thousand and six
ten thirty in the morning
at Temple Beth Shalom
234 Elm Street
Anytown, Anystate
Child's name

With great pride and love
We invite you to share in our joy
when our daughter
Child's name
is called to the Torah as a Bat Mitzvah
on Saturday, June 2, 2006
Place
Address
Parents' Names

We welcome you
to share a special day in our lives
when our daughter
Child's name
is called to the Torah as a Bat Mitzvah
on Saturday, the second of June,
two thousand and six
Place
Address
You are cordially invited to a reception
immediately following the service
Parents' names

Since there are many different family dynamics, the following samples address how parents and/or stepparents names might appear on an invitation. If either parent has remarried it is up to the families to decide whose names will appear on the invitations. It is customary to name the biological parent first when there are stepparents involved.

Married parents
Jane and Harold Levine

The child's name
Susan Lynn Levine

Divorced parents
Jane Levine and Harold Levine
or
Jane Levine
Harold Levine

One parent has remarried
Jane Levine
Harold and Linda Levine

Both parents have remarried
Jane and Sam Stein
Harold and Linda Levine

SAVE THE DATE LETTER OR EMAIL

Dear Friends,

We have a very special event coming up. On Saturday, October 10, 2010, Jay will become a Bar Mitzvah. We are also hosting a party in his honor on Sunday, October 11. Please save these dates.

We hope that you can join us in celebrating this milestone event. A formal invitation will follow closer to the Bar Mitzvah date.

Yours truly,
Parents' Names

LETTER TO NON JEWISH FRIENDS

Dear Friends,

We are sending along this note to explain our customs to our non-Jewish friends. We hope you can join us for this joyous occasion. The bar mitzvah is a coming-of-age ceremony which usually takes place at age thirteen. It is one of the most important Jewish rituals. The bar mitzvah is a symbolic way to usher a child into the adult Jewish community. The child is now old enough to perform mitzvot (the commandments of Jewish life). When a Jewish child becomes a bar or bat mitzvah, he or she publicly reads a section of the Torah, the Five Books of Moses. Each week, every congregation in the Jewish world reads the identical passage. In this way, the youth is linked to the entire Jewish people, regardless of where the thirteen-year-old happens to live. The ultimate message of the service is the triumph of hope, hope for freedom, hope for peace, hope for universal redemption.

It is a time of great celebration. We look forward to sharing our happiness with you. Please let us know if there is anything we can do to help make it possible for you to be with us on this special day. Parents, friends, and siblings are welcome at the synagogue.

We look forward to seeing you.

With best wishes,
Parents' names

* Excerpts from this letter are from <u>Putting God on The Guest List: How to Reclaim the Spiritual Meaning of Your Child's Bar or Bat Mitzvah 2nd Edition</u> © 1996 Jeffery K. Salkin. (Woodstock, VT: Jewish Lights Publishing) Permission granteed by Jewish Lights Publishing, P.O. Box 237, Woodstock, VT 05091 www.jewishlights.com

The candlelighting ceremony is an opportunity to honor special guests. Each individual or group is asked to light one of thirteen candles. The child or parent usually gives a brief explanation of the connection between the honoree (i.e. aunt, teacher) to the Bar/Bat Mitzvah. In order to maintain your guests' attention keep it lively, humorous, poignant and brief. A perfect time to light the candles would be after the meal and before the music and dancing resume.

1.

2.

3.

4.

5.

6.

7.

8.

9.

10.

11.

12.

13.

GUEST	GUEST	GUEST

WELCOME GIFTS

	ITEM	COST
Company		
Contact name		
Phone		
Address		
Email		
Fax		

ACCOMMODATIONS

Hotel/Motel		Hotel/Motel	
Contact name		Contact name	
Phone		Phone	
Address		Address	
Email		Email	
Fax		Fax	

ROOM DESCRIPTION	RATES	ROOM DESCRIPTION	RATES

TRANSPORTATION - RENTAL CARS, VANS / LIMOUSINES / AIRPORTER / BUS

Hotel/Motel		Hotel/Motel	
Contact name		Contact name	
Phone		Phone	
Address		Address	
Email		Email	
Fax		Fax	

VEHICLE DESCRIPTION	RATES	VEHICLE DESCRIPTION	RATES

TABLE 1	TABLE 2	TABLE 3	TABLE 4
1.	1.	1.	1.
2.	2.	2.	2.
3.	3.	3.	3.
4.	4.	4.	4.
5.	5.	5.	5.
6.	6.	6.	6.
7.	7.	7.	7.
8.	8.	8.	8.
9.	9.	9.	9.
10.	10.	10.	10.

TABLE 5	TABLE 6	TABLE 7	TABLE 8
1.	1.	1.	1.
2.	2.	2.	2.
3.	3.	3.	3.
4.	4.	4.	4.
5.	5.	5.	5.
6.	6.	6.	6.
7.	7.	7.	7.
8.	8.	8.	8.
9.	9.	9.	9.
10.	10.	10.	10.

TABLE 9	TABLE 10	TABLE 11	TABLE 12
1.	1.	1.	1.
2.	2.	2.	2.
3.	3.	3.	3.
4.	4.	4.	4.
5.	5.	5.	5.
6.	6.	6.	6.
7.	7.	7.	7.
8.	8.	8.	8.
9.	9.	9.	9.
10.	10.	10.	10.

TABLE 13	TABLE 14	TABLE 15	TABLE 16
1.	1.	1.	1.
2.	2.	2.	2.
3.	3.	3.	3.
4.	4.	4.	4.
5.	5.	5.	5.
6.	6.	6.	6.
7.	7.	7.	7.
8.	8.	8.	8.
9.	9.	9.	9.
10.	10.	10.	10.

TABLE 17	TABLE 18	TABLE 19	TABLE 20
1.	1.	1.	1.
2.	2.	2.	2.
3.	3.	3.	3.
4.	4.	4.	4.
5.	5.	5.	5.
6.	6.	6.	6.
7.	7.	7.	7.
8.	8.	8.	8.
9.	9.	9.	9.
10.	10.	10.	10.

TABLE 21	TABLE 22	TABLE 23	TABLE 24
1.	1.	1.	1.
2.	2.	2.	2.
3.	3.	3.	3.
4.	4.	4.	4.
5.	5.	5.	5.
6.	6.	6.	6.
7.	7.	7.	7.
8.	8.	8.	8.
9.	9.	9.	9.
10.	10.	10.	10.

TABLE 25	TABLE 26	TABLE 27	TABLE 28
1.	1.	1.	1.
2.	2.	2.	2.
3.	3.	3.	3.
4.	4.	4.	4.
5.	5.	5.	5.
6.	6.	6.	6.
7.	7.	7.	7.
8.	8.	8.	8.
9.	9.	9.	9.
10.	10.	10.	10.
TABLE 29	**TABLE 30**	**TABLE 31**	**TABLE 32**
1.	1.	1.	1.
2.	2.	2.	2.
3.	3.	3.	3.
4.	4.	4.	4.
5.	5.	5.	5.
6.	6.	6.	6.
7.	7.	7.	7.
8.	8.	8.	8.
9.	9.	9.	9.
10.	10.	10.	10.
TABLE 33	**TABLE 34**	**TABLE 35**	**TABLE 36**
1.	1.	1.	1.
2.	2.	2.	2.
3.	3.	3.	3.
4.	4.	4.	4.
5.	5.	5.	5.
6.	6.	6.	6.
7.	7.	7.	7.
8.	8.	8.	8.
9.	9.	9.	9.
10.	10.	10.	10.

Name_____

Address_____

Phone_____

Email_____

☐ Invitation sent, date_____

Gift_____

_____

_____

☐ Thank you, date _____

☐ Reception   _____ Adults
                     _____ Children

Table Seating _____ ☐

_____ ☐

_____ ☐

_____ ☐

_____ ☐

_____ ☐

☐ Friday dinner   ☐ Sunday brunch

☐ Out of town guest list, page 45

Name_____

Address_____

Phone_____

Email_____

☐ Invitation sent, date_____

Gift_____

_____

_____

☐ Thank you, date _____

☐ Reception   _____ Adults
                     _____ Children

Table Seating _____ ☐

_____ ☐

_____ ☐

_____ ☐

_____ ☐

_____ ☐

☐ Friday dinner   ☐ Sunday brunch

☐ Out of town guest list, page 45

Name_____

Address_____

Phone_____

Email_____

☐ Invitation sent, date_____

Gift_____

_____

_____

☐ Thank you, date _____

☐ Reception   _____ Adults
                     _____ Children

Table Seating _____ ☐

_____ ☐

_____ ☐

_____ ☐

_____ ☐

_____ ☐

☐ Friday dinner   ☐ Sunday brunch

☐ Out of town guest list, page 45

A

Name_____

_____

Address_____

_____

Phone_____

_____

Email_____

☐ Invitation sent, date_____

Gift_____

_____

_____

☐ Thank you, date _____

☐ Reception   ____ Adults   ____ Children

Table Seating _____ ☐

_____ ☐

_____ ☐

_____ ☐

_____ ☐

_____ ☐

_____ ☐

☐ Friday dinner   ☐ Sunday brunch

☐ Out of town guest list, page 45

Name_____

_____

Address_____

_____

Phone_____

_____

Email_____

☐ Invitation sent, date_____

Gift_____

_____

_____

☐ Thank you, date _____

☐ Reception   ____ Adults   ____ Children

Table Seating _____ ☐

_____ ☐

_____ ☐

_____ ☐

_____ ☐

_____ ☐

_____ ☐

☐ Friday dinner   ☐ Sunday brunch

☐ Out of town guest list, page 45

Name_____

_____

Address_____

_____

Phone_____

_____

Email_____

☐ Invitation sent, date_____

Gift_____

_____

_____

☐ Thank you, date _____

☐ Reception   ____ Adults   ____ Children

Table Seating _____ ☐

_____ ☐

_____ ☐

_____ ☐

_____ ☐

_____ ☐

_____ ☐

☐ Friday dinner   ☐ Sunday brunch

☐ Out of town guest list, page 45

Name_____

_____

Address_____

Phone_____

_____

Email_____

☐ Invitation sent, date_____

Gift_____

_____

_____

☐ Thank you, date _____

☐ Reception   _____ Adults
                _____ Children

Table Seating _____ ☐

_____ ☐

_____ ☐

_____ ☐

_____ ☐

_____ ☐

☐ Friday dinner   ☐ Sunday brunch

☐ Out of town guest list, page 45

Name_____

_____

Address_____

Phone_____

_____

Email_____

☐ Invitation sent, date_____

Gift_____

_____

_____

☐ Thank you, date _____

☐ Reception   _____ Adults
                _____ Children

Table Seating _____ ☐

_____ ☐

_____ ☐

_____ ☐

_____ ☐

_____ ☐

☐ Friday dinner   ☐ Sunday brunch

☐ Out of town guest list, page 45

Name_____

_____

Address_____

Phone_____

_____

Email_____

☐ Invitation sent, date_____

Gift_____

_____

_____

☐ Thank you, date _____

☐ Reception   _____ Adults
                _____ Children

Table Seating _____ ☐

_____ ☐

_____ ☐

_____ ☐

_____ ☐

_____ ☐

☐ Friday dinner   ☐ Sunday brunch

☐ Out of town guest list, page 45

B

Name_____

_____

Address_____

_____

Phone_____

_____

Email_____

☐ Invitation sent, date_____

Gift_____

_____

_____

☐ Thank you, date _____

☐ Reception   _____ Adults
_____ Children

Table Seating _____ ☐

_____ ☐

_____ ☐

_____ ☐

_____ ☐

_____ ☐

_____ ☐

_____ ☐

☐ Friday dinner   ☐ Sunday brunch

☐ Out of town guest list, page 45

Name_____

_____

Address_____

_____

Phone_____

_____

Email_____

☐ Invitation sent, date_____

Gift_____

_____

_____

☐ Thank you, date _____

☐ Reception   _____ Adults
_____ Children

Table Seating _____ ☐

_____ ☐

_____ ☐

_____ ☐

_____ ☐

_____ ☐

_____ ☐

☐ Friday dinner   ☐ Sunday brunch

☐ Out of town guest list, page 45

Name_____

_____

Address_____

_____

Phone_____

_____

Email_____

☐ Invitation sent, date_____

Gift_____

_____

_____

☐ Thank you, date _____

☐ Reception   _____ Adults
_____ Children

Table Seating _____ ☐

_____ ☐

_____ ☐

_____ ☐

_____ ☐

_____ ☐

_____ ☐

☐ Friday dinner   ☐ Sunday brunch

☐ Out of town guest list, page 45

Name_____

_____

Address_____

_____

Phone_____

_____

Email_____

☐ Invitation sent, date_____

Gift_____

_____

_____

☐ Thank you, date _____

☐ Reception   _____ Adults
                   _____ Children

Table Seating _____ ☐

_____ ☐

_____ ☐

_____ ☐

_____ ☐

_____ ☐

_____ ☐

☐ Friday dinner   ☐ Sunday brunch

☐ Out of town guest list, page 45

Name_____

_____

Address_____

_____

Phone_____

_____

Email_____

☐ Invitation sent, date_____

Gift_____

_____

_____

☐ Thank you, date _____

☐ Reception   _____ Adults
                   _____ Children

Table Seating _____ ☐

_____ ☐

_____ ☐

_____ ☐

_____ ☐

_____ ☐

_____ ☐

☐ Friday dinner   ☐ Sunday brunch

☐ Out of town guest list, page 45

Name_____

_____

Address_____

_____

Phone_____

_____

Email_____

☐ Invitation sent, date_____

Gift_____

_____

_____

☐ Thank you, date _____

☐ Reception   _____ Adults
                   _____ Children

Table Seating _____ ☐

_____ ☐

_____ ☐

_____ ☐

_____ ☐

_____ ☐

_____ ☐

☐ Friday dinner   ☐ Sunday brunch

☐ Out of town guest list, page 45

C

Name_____

Address_____

_____

Phone_____

_____

Email_____

☐ Invitation sent, date_____

Gift_____

_____

_____

☐ Thank you, date_____

☐ Reception   ____ Adults   ____ Children

Table Seating _____ ☐

_____ ☐

_____ ☐

_____ ☐

_____ ☐

_____ ☐

_____ ☐

☐ Friday dinner   ☐ Sunday brunch

☐ Out of town guest list, page 45

Name_____

Address_____

_____

Phone_____

_____

Email_____

☐ Invitation sent, date_____

Gift_____

_____

_____

☐ Thank you, date_____

☐ Reception   ____ Adults   ____ Children

Table Seating _____ ☐

_____ ☐

_____ ☐

_____ ☐

_____ ☐

_____ ☐

_____ ☐

☐ Friday dinner   ☐ Sunday brunch

☐ Out of town guest list, page 45

Name_____

Address_____

_____

Phone_____

_____

Email_____

☐ Invitation sent, date_____

Gift_____

_____

_____

☐ Thank you, date_____

☐ Reception   ____ Adults   ____ Children

Table Seating _____ ☐

_____ ☐

_____ ☐

_____ ☐

_____ ☐

_____ ☐

_____ ☐

☐ Friday dinner   ☐ Sunday brunch

☐ Out of town guest list, page 45

Name_____

_____

Address_____

Phone_____

_____

Email_____

☐ Invitation sent, date_____

Gift_____

_____

_____

☐ Thank you, date _____

☐ Reception   _____ Adults
_____ Children

Table Seating _____ ☐

_____ ☐

_____ ☐

_____ ☐

_____ ☐

_____ ☐

_____ ☐

☐ Friday dinner   ☐ Sunday brunch

☐ Out of town guest list, page 45

Name_____

_____

Address_____

Phone_____

_____

Email_____

☐ Invitation sent, date_____

Gift_____

_____

_____

☐ Thank you, date _____

☐ Reception   _____ Adults
_____ Children

Table Seating _____ ☐

_____ ☐

_____ ☐

_____ ☐

_____ ☐

_____ ☐

_____ ☐

☐ Friday dinner   ☐ Sunday brunch

☐ Out of town guest list, page 45

Name_____

_____

Address_____

Phone_____

_____

Email_____

☐ Invitation sent, date_____

Gift_____

_____

_____

☐ Thank you, date _____

☐ Reception   _____ Adults
_____ Children

Table Seating _____ ☐

_____ ☐

_____ ☐

_____ ☐

_____ ☐

_____ ☐

_____ ☐

☐ Friday dinner   ☐ Sunday brunch

☐ Out of town guest list, page 45

D

Name_____

Address_____

_____

Phone_____

Email_____

☐ Invitation sent, date_____

Gift_____

_____

_____

☐ Thank you, date _____

☐ Reception ____ Adults
              ____ Children

Table Seating _____ ☐
              _____ ☐
              _____ ☐
              _____ ☐
              _____ ☐
              _____ ☐
              _____ ☐

☐ Friday dinner   ☐ Sunday brunch

☐ Out of town guest list, page 45

Name_____

Address_____

_____

Phone_____

_____

Email_____

☐ Invitation sent, date_____

Gift_____

_____

_____

☐ Thank you, date _____

☐ Reception ____ Adults
              ____ Children

Table Seating _____ ☐
              _____ ☐
              _____ ☐
              _____ ☐
              _____ ☐
              _____ ☐
              _____ ☐

☐ Friday dinner   ☐ Sunday brunch

☐ Out of town guest list, page 45

Name_____

_____

Address_____

Phone_____

_____

Email_____

☐ Invitation sent, date_____

Gift_____

_____

☐ Thank you, date _____

☐ Reception ____ Adults
              ____ Children

Table Seating _____ ☐
              _____ ☐
              _____ ☐
              _____ ☐
              _____ ☐
              _____ ☐

☐ Friday dinner   ☐ Sunday brunch

☐ Out of town guest list, page 45

Name_____

_____

Address_____

_____

Phone_____

_____

Email_____

☐ Invitation sent, date_____

Gift_____

_____

_____

☐ Thank you, date _____

☐ Reception   ____ Adults
                   ____ Children

Table Seating _____ ☐

_____ ☐

_____ ☐

_____ ☐

_____ ☐

_____ ☐

_____ ☐

☐ Friday dinner   ☐ Sunday brunch

☐ Out of town guest list, page 45

Name_____

_____

Address_____

_____

Phone_____

_____

Email_____

☐ Invitation sent, date_____

Gift_____

_____

_____

☐ Thank you, date _____

☐ Reception   ____ Adults
                   ____ Children

Table Seating _____ ☐

_____ ☐

_____ ☐

_____ ☐

_____ ☐

_____ ☐

_____ ☐

☐ Friday dinner   ☐ Sunday brunch

☐ Out of town guest list, page 45

Name_____

_____

Address_____

_____

Phone_____

_____

Email_____

☐ Invitation sent, date_____

Gift_____

_____

_____

☐ Thank you, date _____

☐ Reception   ____ Adults
                   ____ Children

Table Seating _____ ☐

_____ ☐

_____ ☐

_____ ☐

_____ ☐

_____ ☐

☐ Friday dinner   ☐ Sunday brunch

☐ Out of town guest list, page 45

E

Name

Address

Phone

Email

☐ Invitation sent, date

Gift

☐ Thank you, date

☐ Reception   _____ Adults
               _____ Children
Table Seating _____

☐ Friday dinner   ☐ Sunday brunch
☐ Out of town guest list, page 45

Name

Address

Phone

Email

☐ Invitation sent, date

Gift

☐ Thank you, date

☐ Reception   _____ Adults
               _____ Children
Table Seating _____

☐ Friday dinner   ☐ Sunday brunch
☐ Out of town guest list, page 45

Name

Address

Phone

Email

☐ Invitation sent, date

Gift

☐ Thank you, date

☐ Reception   _____ Adults
               _____ Children
Table Seating _____

☐ Friday dinner   ☐ Sunday brunch
☐ Out of town guest list, page 45

Name _____
_____
Address _____
_____
Phone _____
_____
Email _____
☐ Invitation sent, date _____
Gift _____
_____
_____
☐ Thank you, date _____

☐ Reception   ____ Adults
                     ____ Children
Table Seating _____ ☐
_____ ☐
_____ ☐
_____ ☐
_____ ☐
_____ ☐
_____ ☐

☐ Friday dinner   ☐ Sunday brunch
☐ Out of town guest list, page 45

Name _____
_____
Address _____
_____
Phone _____
_____
Email _____
☐ Invitation sent, date _____
Gift _____
_____
_____
☐ Thank you, date _____

☐ Reception   ____ Adults
                     ____ Children
Table Seating _____ ☐
_____ ☐
_____ ☐
_____ ☐
_____ ☐
_____ ☐
_____ ☐

☐ Friday dinner   ☐ Sunday brunch
☐ Out of town guest list, page 45

Name _____
_____
Address _____
_____
Phone _____
_____
Email _____
☐ Invitation sent, date _____
Gift _____
_____
_____
☐ Thank you, date _____

☐ Reception   ____ Adults
                     ____ Children
Table Seating _____ ☐
_____ ☐
_____ ☐
_____ ☐
_____ ☐
_____ ☐
_____ ☐

☐ Friday dinner   ☐ Sunday brunch
☐ Out of town guest list, page 45

Name_____

Address_____

Phone_____

Email_____

☐ Invitation sent, date_____

Gift_____

_____

☐ Thank you, date_____

☐ Reception   ____ Adults   ____ Children

Table Seating _____ ☐

_____ ☐

_____ ☐

_____ ☐

_____ ☐

_____ ☐

_____ ☐

☐ Friday dinner   ☐ Sunday brunch

☐ Out of town guest list, page 45

F

Name_____

Address_____

Phone_____

Email_____

☐ Invitation sent, date_____

Gift_____

_____

☐ Thank you, date_____

☐ Reception   ____ Adults   ____ Children

Table Seating _____ ☐

_____ ☐

_____ ☐

_____ ☐

_____ ☐

_____ ☐

_____ ☐

☐ Friday dinner   ☐ Sunday brunch

☐ Out of town guest list, page 45

Name_____

Address_____

Phone_____

Email_____

☐ Invitation sent, date_____

Gift_____

_____

☐ Thank you, date_____

☐ Reception   ____ Adults   ____ Children

Table Seating _____ ☐

_____ ☐

_____ ☐

_____ ☐

_____ ☐

_____ ☐

_____ ☐

☐ Friday dinner   ☐ Sunday brunch

☐ Out of town guest list, page 45

Name_____

_____

Address_____

_____

Phone_____

_____

Email_____

☐ Invitation sent, date_____

Gift_____

_____

_____

☐ Thank you, date _____

☐ Reception   ____ Adults   ____ Children

Table Seating _____ ☐

_____ ☐

_____ ☐

_____ ☐

_____ ☐

_____ ☐

☐ Friday dinner   ☐ Sunday brunch

☐ Out of town guest list, page 45

Name_____

_____

Address_____

_____

Phone_____

_____

Email_____

☐ Invitation sent, date_____

Gift_____

_____

_____

☐ Thank you, date _____

☐ Reception   ____ Adults   ____ Children

Table Seating _____ ☐

_____ ☐

_____ ☐

_____ ☐

_____ ☐

_____ ☐

☐ Friday dinner   ☐ Sunday brunch

☐ Out of town guest list, page 45

Name_____

_____

Address_____

_____

Phone_____

_____

Email_____

☐ Invitation sent, date_____

Gift_____

_____

_____

☐ Thank you, date _____

☐ Reception   ____ Adults   ____ Children

Table Seating _____ ☐

_____ ☐

_____ ☐

_____ ☐

_____ ☐

_____ ☐

☐ Friday dinner   ☐ Sunday brunch

☐ Out of town guest list, page 45

Name_____

Address_____

_____

Phone_____

_____

Email_____

☐ Invitation sent, date_____

Gift_____

_____

_____

☐ Thank you, date _____

☐ Reception   _____ Adults
              _____ Children

Table Seating _____ ☐

_____ ☐

_____ ☐

_____ ☐

_____ ☐

_____ ☐

_____ ☐

☐ Friday dinner   ☐ Sunday brunch

☐ Out of town guest list, page 45

G

Name_____

Address_____

_____

Phone_____

_____

Email_____

☐ Invitation sent, date_____

Gift_____

_____

_____

☐ Thank you, date _____

☐ Reception   _____ Adults
              _____ Children

Table Seating _____ ☐

_____ ☐

_____ ☐

_____ ☐

_____ ☐

_____ ☐

_____ ☐

☐ Friday dinner   ☐ Sunday brunch

☐ Out of town guest list, page 45

Name_____

Address_____

_____

Phone_____

_____

Email_____

☐ Invitation sent, date_____

Gift_____

_____

_____

☐ Thank you, date _____

☐ Reception   _____ Adults
              _____ Children

Table Seating _____ ☐

_____ ☐

_____ ☐

_____ ☐

_____ ☐

_____ ☐

☐ Friday dinner   ☐ Sunday brunch

☐ Out of town guest list, page 45

Name _____

Address _____

Phone _____

Email _____

☐ Invitation sent, date _____

Gift _____

_____

_____

☐ Thank you, date _____

☐ Reception   ____ Adults   ____ Children

Table Seating _____ ☐

_____ ☐

_____ ☐

_____ ☐

_____ ☐

_____ ☐

_____ ☐

☐ Friday dinner   ☐ Sunday brunch

☐ Out of town guest list, page 45

Name _____

Address _____

Phone _____

Email _____

☐ Invitation sent, date _____

Gift _____

_____

_____

☐ Thank you, date _____

☐ Reception   ____ Adults   ____ Children

Table Seating _____ ☐

_____ ☐

_____ ☐

_____ ☐

_____ ☐

_____ ☐

_____ ☐

☐ Friday dinner   ☐ Sunday brunch

☐ Out of town guest list, page 45

Name _____

Address _____

Phone _____

Email _____

☐ Invitation sent, date _____

Gift _____

_____

_____

☐ Thank you, date _____

☐ Reception   ____ Adults   ____ Children

Table Seating _____ ☐

_____ ☐

_____ ☐

_____ ☐

_____ ☐

_____ ☐

_____ ☐

☐ Friday dinner   ☐ Sunday brunch

☐ Out of town guest list, page 45

Name_____

_____

Address_____

_____

Phone_____

_____

Email_____

☐ Invitation sent, date_____

Gift_____

_____

_____

☐ Thank you, date _____

☐ Reception   _____ Adults
                   _____ Children

Table Seating _____ ☐

_____ ☐

_____ ☐

_____ ☐

_____ ☐

_____ ☐

_____ ☐

☐ Friday dinner   ☐ Sunday brunch

☐ Out of town guest list, page 45

H

Name_____

_____

Address_____

_____

Phone_____

_____

Email_____

☐ Invitation sent, date_____

Gift_____

_____

_____

☐ Thank you, date _____

☐ Reception   _____ Adults
                   _____ Children

Table Seating _____ ☐

_____ ☐

_____ ☐

_____ ☐

_____ ☐

_____ ☐

_____ ☐

☐ Friday dinner   ☐ Sunday brunch

☐ Out of town guest list, page 45

Name_____

_____

Address_____

_____

Phone_____

_____

Email_____

☐ Invitation sent, date_____

Gift_____

_____

_____

☐ Thank you, date _____

☐ Reception   _____ Adults
                   _____ Children

Table Seating _____ ☐

_____ ☐

_____ ☐

_____ ☐

_____ ☐

_____ ☐

_____ ☐

☐ Friday dinner   ☐ Sunday brunch

☐ Out of town guest list, page 45

Name_____

_____

Address_____

_____

Phone_____

_____

Email_____

☐ Invitation sent, date_____

Gift_____

_____

_____

☐ Thank you, date _____

☐ Reception   _____ Adults
               _____ Children

Table Seating _____ ☐

_____ ☐

_____ ☐

_____ ☐

_____ ☐

_____ ☐

_____ ☐

☐ Friday dinner   ☐ Sunday brunch

☐ Out of town guest list, page 45

Name_____

_____

Address_____

_____

Phone_____

_____

Email_____

☐ Invitation sent, date_____

Gift_____

_____

_____

☐ Thank you, date _____

☐ Reception   _____ Adults
               _____ Children

Table Seating _____ ☐

_____ ☐

_____ ☐

_____ ☐

_____ ☐

_____ ☐

_____ ☐

☐ Friday dinner   ☐ Sunday brunch

☐ Out of town guest list, page 45

Name_____

_____

Address_____

_____

Phone_____

_____

Email_____

☐ Invitation sent, date_____

Gift_____

_____

_____

☐ Thank you, date _____

☐ Reception   _____ Adults
               _____ Children

Table Seating _____ ☐

_____ ☐

_____ ☐

_____ ☐

_____ ☐

_____ ☐

_____ ☐

☐ Friday dinner   ☐ Sunday brunch

☐ Out of town guest list, page 45

Name_____

Address_____

Phone_____

Email_____

☐ Invitation sent, date_____

Gift_____

_____

_____

☐ Thank you, date _____

☐ Reception ____ Adults
____ Children

Table Seating _____ ☐
_____ ☐
_____ ☐
_____ ☐
_____ ☐
_____ ☐
_____ ☐

☐ Friday dinner   ☐ Sunday brunch
☐ Out of town guest list, page 45

I

Name_____

Address_____

Phone_____

Email_____

☐ Invitation sent, date_____

Gift_____

_____

_____

☐ Thank you, date _____

☐ Reception ____ Adults
____ Children

Table Seating _____ ☐
_____ ☐
_____ ☐
_____ ☐
_____ ☐
_____ ☐
_____ ☐

☐ Friday dinner   ☐ Sunday brunch
☐ Out of town guest list, page 45

Name_____

Address_____

Phone_____

Email_____

☐ Invitation sent, date_____

Gift_____

_____

_____

☐ Thank you, date _____

☐ Reception ____ Adults
____ Children

Table Seating _____ ☐
_____ ☐
_____ ☐
_____ ☐
_____ ☐
_____ ☐
_____ ☐

☐ Friday dinner   ☐ Sunday brunch
☐ Out of town guest list, page 45

Name_____

_____

Address_____

_____

Phone_____

_____

Email_____

☐ Invitation sent, date_____

Gift_____

_____

_____

☐ Thank you, date _____

☐ Reception   _____ Adults
                   _____ Children
Table Seating _____ ☐

_____ ☐

_____ ☐

_____ ☐

_____ ☐

_____ ☐

_____ ☐

☐ Friday dinner   ☐ Sunday brunch

☐ Out of town guest list, page 45

Name_____

_____

Address_____

_____

Phone_____

_____

Email_____

☐ Invitation sent, date_____

Gift_____

_____

_____

☐ Thank you, date _____

☐ Reception   _____ Adults
                   _____ Children
Table Seating _____ ☐

_____ ☐

_____ ☐

_____ ☐

_____ ☐

_____ ☐

_____ ☐

☐ Friday dinner   ☐ Sunday brunch

☐ Out of town guest list, page 45

Name_____

_____

Address_____

_____

Phone_____

_____

Email_____

☐ Invitation sent, date_____

Gift_____

_____

_____

☐ Thank you, date _____

☐ Reception   _____ Adults
                   _____ Children
Table Seating _____ ☐

_____ ☐

_____ ☐

_____ ☐

_____ ☐

_____ ☐

_____ ☐

☐ Friday dinner   ☐ Sunday brunch

☐ Out of town guest list, page 45

Name_____

Address_____

Phone_____

Email_____

☐ Invitation sent, date_____

Gift_____

☐ Thank you, date_____

☐ Reception   _____ Adults
                    _____ Children

Table Seating _____ ☐
                  _____ ☐
                  _____ ☐
                  _____ ☐
                  _____ ☐
                  _____ ☐
                  _____ ☐

☐ Friday dinner   ☐ Sunday brunch
☐ Out of town guest list, page 45

Name_____

Address_____

Phone_____

Email_____

☐ Invitation sent, date_____

Gift_____

☐ Thank you, date_____

☐ Reception   _____ Adults
                    _____ Children

Table Seating _____ ☐
                  _____ ☐
                  _____ ☐
                  _____ ☐
                  _____ ☐
                  _____ ☐
                  _____ ☐

☐ Friday dinner   ☐ Sunday brunch
☐ Out of town guest list, page 45

J

Name_____

Address_____

Phone_____

Email_____

☐ Invitation sent, date_____

Gift_____

☐ Thank you, date_____

☐ Reception   _____ Adults
                    _____ Children

Table Seating _____ ☐
                  _____ ☐
                  _____ ☐
                  _____ ☐
                  _____ ☐
                  _____ ☐
                  _____ ☐

☐ Friday dinner   ☐ Sunday brunch
☐ Out of town guest list, page 45

Name_____

Address_____

Phone_____

Email_____

☐ Invitation sent, date_____

Gift_____

_____

☐ Thank you, date _____

☐ Reception ____ Adults
____ Children

Table Seating _____ ☐

_____ ☐
_____ ☐
_____ ☐
_____ ☐
_____ ☐
_____ ☐

☐ Friday dinner   ☐ Sunday brunch
☐ Out of town guest list, page 45

Name_____

Address_____

Phone_____

Email_____

☐ Invitation sent, date_____

Gift_____

_____

☐ Thank you, date _____

☐ Reception ____ Adults
____ Children

Table Seating _____ ☐

_____ ☐
_____ ☐
_____ ☐
_____ ☐
_____ ☐
_____ ☐

☐ Friday dinner   ☐ Sunday brunch
☐ Out of town guest list, page 45

Name_____

Address_____

Phone_____

Email_____

☐ Invitation sent, date_____

Gift_____

_____

☐ Thank you, date _____

☐ Reception ____ Adults
____ Children

Table Seating _____ ☐

_____ ☐
_____ ☐
_____ ☐
_____ ☐
_____ ☐
_____ ☐

☐ Friday dinner   ☐ Sunday brunch
☐ Out of town guest list, page 45

Name_____

_____

Address_____

_____

Phone_____

_____

Email_____

☐ Invitation sent, date_____

Gift_____

_____

_____

☐ Thank you, date_____

☐ Reception _____ Adults _____ Children

Table Seating _____ ☐

_____ ☐

_____ ☐

_____ ☐

_____ ☐

_____ ☐

_____ ☐

☐ Friday dinner   ☐ Sunday brunch

☐ Out of town guest list, page 45

Name_____

_____

Address_____

_____

Phone_____

_____

Email_____

☐ Invitation sent, date_____

Gift_____

_____

_____

☐ Thank you, date_____

☐ Reception _____ Adults _____ Children

Table Seating _____ ☐

_____ ☐

_____ ☐

_____ ☐

_____ ☐

_____ ☐

_____ ☐

☐ Friday dinner   ☐ Sunday brunch

☐ Out of town guest list, page 45

K

Name_____

_____

Address_____

_____

Phone_____

_____

Email_____

☐ Invitation sent, date_____

Gift_____

_____

_____

☐ Thank you, date_____

☐ Reception _____ Adults _____ Children

Table Seating _____ ☐

_____ ☐

_____ ☐

_____ ☐

_____ ☐

_____ ☐

_____ ☐

☐ Friday dinner   ☐ Sunday brunch

☐ Out of town guest list, page 45

Name_____

_____

Address_____

_____

Phone_____

_____

Email_____

☐ Invitation sent, date_____

Gift_____

_____

_____

☐ Thank you, date _____

☐ Reception   ____ Adults
                     ____ Children

Table Seating _____ ☐

_____ ☐

_____ ☐

_____ ☐

_____ ☐

_____ ☐

_____ ☐

☐ Friday dinner   ☐ Sunday brunch

☐ Out of town guest list, page 45

Name_____

_____

Address_____

_____

Phone_____

_____

Email_____

☐ Invitation sent, date_____

Gift_____

_____

_____

☐ Thank you, date _____

☐ Reception   ____ Adults
                     ____ Children

Table Seating _____ ☐

_____ ☐

_____ ☐

_____ ☐

_____ ☐

_____ ☐

_____ ☐

☐ Friday dinner   ☐ Sunday brunch

☐ Out of town guest list, page 45

Name_____

_____

Address_____

_____

Phone_____

_____

Email_____

☐ Invitation sent, date_____

Gift_____

_____

_____

☐ Thank you, date _____

☐ Reception   ____ Adults
                     ____ Children

Table Seating _____ ☐

_____ ☐

_____ ☐

_____ ☐

_____ ☐

_____ ☐

_____ ☐

☐ Friday dinner   ☐ Sunday brunch

☐ Out of town guest list, page 45

Name _____

_____

Address _____

_____

Phone _____

_____

Email _____

☐ Invitation sent, date _____

Gift _____

_____

_____

☐ Thank you, date _____

☐ Reception   _____ Adults   _____ Children

Table Seating _____ ☐

_____ ☐

_____ ☐

_____ ☐

_____ ☐

_____ ☐

_____ ☐

☐ Friday dinner   ☐ Sunday brunch

☐ Out of town guest list, page 45

Name _____

_____

Address _____

_____

Phone _____

_____

Email _____

☐ Invitation sent, date _____

Gift _____

_____

_____

☐ Thank you, date _____

☐ Reception   _____ Adults   _____ Children

Table Seating _____ ☐

_____ ☐

_____ ☐

_____ ☐

_____ ☐

_____ ☐

_____ ☐

☐ Friday dinner   ☐ Sunday brunch

☐ Out of town guest list, page 45

L

Name _____

_____

Address _____

_____

Phone _____

_____

Email _____

☐ Invitation sent, date _____

Gift _____

_____

_____

☐ Thank you, date _____

☐ Reception   _____ Adults   _____ Children

Table Seating _____ ☐

_____ ☐

_____ ☐

_____ ☐

_____ ☐

_____ ☐

_____ ☐

☐ Friday dinner   ☐ Sunday brunch

☐ Out of town guest list, page 45

Name_____

_____

Address_____

_____

Phone_____

_____

Email_____

☐ Invitation sent, date_____

Gift_____

_____

_____

☐ Thank you, date _____

☐ Reception _____ Adults

_____ Children

Table Seating _____ ☐

_____ ☐

_____ ☐

_____ ☐

_____ ☐

_____ ☐

_____ ☐

☐ Friday dinner ☐ Sunday brunch

☐ Out of town guest list, page 45

Name_____

_____

Address_____

_____

Phone_____

_____

Email_____

☐ Invitation sent, date_____

Gift_____

_____

_____

☐ Thank you, date _____

☐ Reception _____ Adults

_____ Children

Table Seating _____ ☐

_____ ☐

_____ ☐

_____ ☐

_____ ☐

_____ ☐

☐ Friday dinner ☐ Sunday brunch

☐ Out of town guest list, page 45

Name_____

_____

Address_____

_____

Phone_____

_____

Email_____

☐ Invitation sent, date_____

Gift_____

_____

_____

☐ Thank you, date _____

☐ Reception _____ Adults

_____ Children

Table Seating _____ ☐

_____ ☐

_____ ☐

_____ ☐

_____ ☐

_____ ☐

☐ Friday dinner ☐ Sunday brunch

☐ Out of town guest list, page 45

Name_____

Address_____

_____

Phone_____

_____

Email_____

☐ Invitation sent, date_____

Gift_____

_____

_____

☐ Thank you, date _____

☐ Reception   ____ Adults
                 ____ Children

Table Seating _____ ☐

_____ ☐

_____ ☐

_____ ☐

_____ ☐

_____ ☐

_____ ☐

☐ Friday dinner   ☐ Sunday brunch

☐ Out of town guest list, page 45

Name_____

_____

Address_____

_____

Phone_____

_____

Email_____

☐ Invitation sent, date_____

Gift_____

_____

_____

☐ Thank you, date _____

☐ Reception   ____ Adults
                 ____ Children

Table Seating _____ ☐

_____ ☐

_____ ☐

_____ ☐

_____ ☐

_____ ☐

_____ ☐

☐ Friday dinner   ☐ Sunday brunch

☐ Out of town guest list, page 45

M

Name_____

_____

Address_____

_____

Phone_____

_____

Email_____

☐ Invitation sent, date_____

Gift_____

_____

_____

☐ Thank you, date _____

☐ Reception   ____ Adults
                 ____ Children

Table Seating _____ ☐

_____ ☐

_____ ☐

_____ ☐

_____ ☐

_____ ☐

_____ ☐

☐ Friday dinner   ☐ Sunday brunch

☐ Out of town guest list, page 45

Name_____

Address_____

_____

Phone_____

_____

Email_____

☐ Invitation sent, date_____

Gift_____

_____

_____

☐ Thank you, date_____

☐ Reception   _____ Adults
                _____ Children

Table Seating _____ ☐
              _____ ☐
              _____ ☐
              _____ ☐
              _____ ☐
              _____ ☐
              _____ ☐

☐ Friday dinner   ☐ Sunday brunch

☐ Out of town guest list, page 45

Name_____

Address_____

_____

Phone_____

_____

Email_____

☐ Invitation sent, date_____

Gift_____

_____

_____

☐ Thank you, date_____

☐ Reception   _____ Adults
                _____ Children

Table Seating _____ ☐
              _____ ☐
              _____ ☐
              _____ ☐
              _____ ☐
              _____ ☐
              _____ ☐

☐ Friday dinner   ☐ Sunday brunch

☐ Out of town guest list, page 45

Name_____

Address_____

_____

Phone_____

_____

Email_____

☐ Invitation sent, date_____

Gift_____

_____

_____

☐ Thank you, date_____

☐ Reception   _____ Adults
                _____ Children

Table Seating _____ ☐
              _____ ☐
              _____ ☐
              _____ ☐
              _____ ☐
              _____ ☐
              _____ ☐

☐ Friday dinner   ☐ Sunday brunch

☐ Out of town guest list, page 45

Name _____

Address _____

_____

Phone _____

_____

Email _____

☐ Invitation sent, date _____

Gift _____

_____

_____

☐ Thank you, date _____

☐ Reception   _____ Adults
       _____ Children

Table Seating _____ ☐

_____ ☐

_____ ☐

_____ ☐

_____ ☐

_____ ☐

_____ ☐

☐ Friday dinner   ☐ Sunday brunch

☐ Out of town guest list, page 45

Name _____

Address _____

_____

Phone _____

_____

Email _____

☐ Invitation sent, date _____

Gift _____

_____

_____

☐ Thank you, date _____

☐ Reception   _____ Adults
       _____ Children

Table Seating _____ ☐

_____ ☐

_____ ☐

_____ ☐

_____ ☐

_____ ☐

_____ ☐

☐ Friday dinner   ☐ Sunday brunch

☐ Out of town guest list, page 45

N

Name _____

Address _____

_____

Phone _____

_____

Email _____

☐ Invitation sent, date _____

Gift _____

_____

_____

☐ Thank you, date _____

☐ Reception   _____ Adults
       _____ Children

Table Seating _____ ☐

_____ ☐

_____ ☐

_____ ☐

_____ ☐

_____ ☐

_____ ☐

☐ Friday dinner   ☐ Sunday brunch

☐ Out of town guest list, page 45

Name_____

Address_____

Phone_____

Email_____

☐ Invitation sent, date_____

Gift_____

_____

_____

☐ Thank you, date_____

☐ Reception   ____ Adults
                ____ Children

Table Seating _____ ☐

_____ ☐

_____ ☐

_____ ☐

_____ ☐

_____ ☐

_____ ☐

☐ Friday dinner   ☐ Sunday brunch

☐ Out of town guest list, page 45

Name_____

Address_____

Phone_____

Email_____

☐ Invitation sent, date_____

Gift_____

_____

_____

☐ Thank you, date_____

☐ Reception   ____ Adults
                ____ Children

Table Seating _____ ☐

_____ ☐

_____ ☐

_____ ☐

_____ ☐

_____ ☐

_____ ☐

☐ Friday dinner   ☐ Sunday brunch

☐ Out of town guest list, page 45

Name_____

Address_____

Phone_____

Email_____

☐ Invitation sent, date_____

Gift_____

_____

_____

☐ Thank you, date_____

☐ Reception   ____ Adults
                ____ Children

Table Seating _____ ☐

_____ ☐

_____ ☐

_____ ☐

_____ ☐

_____ ☐

☐ Friday dinner   ☐ Sunday brunch

☐ Out of town guest list, page 45

Name_____

Address_____

_____

Phone_____

_____

Email_____

☐ Invitation sent, date_____

Gift_____

_____

_____

☐ Thank you, date_____

☐ Reception ____ Adults
____ Children

Table Seating_____ ☐

_____ ☐

_____ ☐

_____ ☐

_____ ☐

_____ ☐

_____ ☐

☐ Friday dinner   ☐ Sunday brunch

☐ Out of town guest list, page 45

Name_____

Address_____

_____

Phone_____

_____

Email_____

☐ Invitation sent, date_____

Gift_____

_____

_____

☐ Thank you, date_____

☐ Reception ____ Adults
____ Children

Table Seating_____ ☐

_____ ☐

_____ ☐

_____ ☐

_____ ☐

_____ ☐

_____ ☐

☐ Friday dinner   ☐ Sunday brunch

☐ Out of town guest list, page 45

O

Name_____

Address_____

_____

Phone_____

_____

Email_____

☐ Invitation sent, date_____

Gift_____

_____

_____

☐ Thank you, date_____

☐ Reception ____ Adults
____ Children

Table Seating_____ ☐

_____ ☐

_____ ☐

_____ ☐

_____ ☐

_____ ☐

_____ ☐

☐ Friday dinner   ☐ Sunday brunch

☐ Out of town guest list, page 45

Name_____

_____

Address_____

_____

Phone_____

_____

Email_____

☐ Invitation sent, date_____

Gift_____

_____

_____

☐ Thank you, date _____

☐ Reception _____ Adults

_____ Children

Table Seating _____ ☐

_____ ☐

_____ ☐

_____ ☐

_____ ☐

_____ ☐

☐ Friday dinner   ☐ Sunday brunch

☐ Out of town guest list, page 45

Name_____

_____

Address_____

_____

Phone_____

_____

Email_____

☐ Invitation sent, date_____

Gift_____

_____

_____

☐ Thank you, date _____

☐ Reception _____ Adults

_____ Children

Table Seating _____ ☐

_____ ☐

_____ ☐

_____ ☐

_____ ☐

_____ ☐

☐ Friday dinner   ☐ Sunday brunch

☐ Out of town guest list, page 45

Name_____

_____

Address_____

_____

Phone_____

_____

Email_____

☐ Invitation sent, date_____

Gift_____

_____

_____

☐ Thank you, date _____

☐ Reception _____ Adults

_____ Children

Table Seating _____ ☐

_____ ☐

_____ ☐

_____ ☐

_____ ☐

_____ ☐

☐ Friday dinner   ☐ Sunday brunch

☐ Out of town guest list, page 45

Name_____

Address_____

_____

Phone_____

_____

Email_____

☐ Invitation sent, date_____

Gift_____

_____

_____

☐ Thank you, date _____

☐ Reception   _____ Adults
                _____ Children

Table Seating _____ ☐

_____ ☐

_____ ☐

_____ ☐

_____ ☐

_____ ☐

_____ ☐

☐ Friday dinner   ☐ Sunday brunch

☐ Out of town guest list, page 45

Name_____

Address_____

_____

Phone_____

_____

Email_____

☐ Invitation sent, date_____

Gift_____

_____

_____

☐ Thank you, date _____

☐ Reception   _____ Adults
                _____ Children

Table Seating _____ ☐

_____ ☐

_____ ☐

_____ ☐

_____ ☐

_____ ☐

_____ ☐

☐ Friday dinner   ☐ Sunday brunch

☐ Out of town guest list, page 45

P

Name_____

Address_____

_____

Phone_____

_____

Email_____

☐ Invitation sent, date_____

Gift_____

_____

_____

☐ Thank you, date _____

☐ Reception   _____ Adults
                _____ Children

Table Seating _____ ☐

_____ ☐

_____ ☐

_____ ☐

_____ ☐

_____ ☐

_____ ☐

☐ Friday dinner   ☐ Sunday brunch

☐ Out of town guest list, page 45

Name_____

_____

Address_____

_____

Phone_____

_____

Email_____

☐ Invitation sent, date_____

Gift_____

_____

_____

☐ Thank you, date _____

☐ Reception   _____ Adults
              _____ Children

Table Seating _____ ☐

_____ ☐

_____ ☐

_____ ☐

_____ ☐

_____ ☐

_____ ☐

☐ Friday dinner   ☐ Sunday brunch

☐ Out of town guest list, page 45

Name_____

_____

Address_____

_____

Phone_____

_____

Email_____

☐ Invitation sent, date_____

Gift_____

_____

_____

☐ Thank you, date _____

☐ Reception   _____ Adults
              _____ Children

Table Seating _____ ☐

_____ ☐

_____ ☐

_____ ☐

_____ ☐

_____ ☐

_____ ☐

☐ Friday dinner   ☐ Sunday brunch

☐ Out of town guest list, page 45

Name_____

_____

Address_____

_____

Phone_____

_____

Email_____

☐ Invitation sent, date_____

Gift_____

_____

_____

☐ Thank you, date _____

☐ Reception   _____ Adults
              _____ Children

Table Seating _____ ☐

_____ ☐

_____ ☐

_____ ☐

_____ ☐

_____ ☐

_____ ☐

☐ Friday dinner   ☐ Sunday brunch

☐ Out of town guest list, page 45

Name _____

Address _____

_____

Phone _____

_____

Email _____

☐ Invitation sent, date _____

Gift _____

_____

_____

☐ Thank you, date _____

☐ Reception   _____ Adults   _____ Children

Table Seating _____ ☐

_____ ☐

_____ ☐

_____ ☐

_____ ☐

_____ ☐

_____ ☐

☐ Friday dinner   ☐ Sunday brunch

☐ Out of town guest list, page 45

Name _____

Address _____

_____

Phone _____

_____

Email _____

☐ Invitation sent, date _____

Gift _____

_____

_____

☐ Thank you, date _____

☐ Reception   _____ Adults   _____ Children

Table Seating _____ ☐

_____ ☐

_____ ☐

_____ ☐

_____ ☐

_____ ☐

_____ ☐

☐ Friday dinner   ☐ Sunday brunch

☐ Out of town guest list, page 45

Q

Name _____

Address _____

_____

Phone _____

_____

Email _____

☐ Invitation sent, date _____

Gift _____

_____

_____

☐ Thank you, date _____

☐ Reception   _____ Adults   _____ Children

Table Seating _____ ☐

_____ ☐

_____ ☐

_____ ☐

_____ ☐

_____ ☐

_____ ☐

☐ Friday dinner   ☐ Sunday brunch

☐ Out of town guest list, page 45

Name _____

_____

Address _____

_____

Phone _____

_____

Email _____

☐ Invitation sent, date _____

Gift _____

_____

_____

☐ Thank you, date _____

☐ Reception   _____ Adults
               _____ Children

Table Seating _____ ☐

_____ ☐

_____ ☐

_____ ☐

_____ ☐

_____ ☐

_____ ☐

☐ Friday dinner   ☐ Sunday brunch

☐ Out of town guest list, page 45

Name _____

_____

Address _____

_____

Phone _____

_____

Email _____

☐ Invitation sent, date _____

Gift _____

_____

_____

☐ Thank you, date _____

☐ Reception   _____ Adults
               _____ Children

Table Seating _____ ☐

_____ ☐

_____ ☐

_____ ☐

_____ ☐

_____ ☐

☐ Friday dinner   ☐ Sunday brunch

☐ Out of town guest list, page 45

Name _____

_____

Address _____

_____

Phone _____

_____

Email _____

☐ Invitation sent, date _____

Gift _____

_____

_____

☐ Thank you, date _____

☐ Reception   _____ Adults
               _____ Children

Table Seating _____ ☐

_____ ☐

_____ ☐

_____ ☐

_____ ☐

_____ ☐

☐ Friday dinner   ☐ Sunday brunch

☐ Out of town guest list, page 45

Name_____

Address_____

Phone_____

Email_____

☐ Invitation sent, date_____

Gift_____

_____

_____

☐ Thank you, date_____

☐ Reception   ____ Adults
              ____ Children

Table Seating_____ ☐
_____ ☐
_____ ☐
_____ ☐
_____ ☐
_____ ☐
_____ ☐

☐ Friday dinner   ☐ Sunday brunch
☐ Out of town guest list, page 45

Name_____

Address_____

Phone_____

Email_____

☐ Invitation sent, date_____

Gift_____

_____

_____

☐ Thank you, date_____

☐ Reception   ____ Adults
              ____ Children

Table Seating_____ ☐
_____ ☐
_____ ☐
_____ ☐
_____ ☐
_____ ☐
_____ ☐

☐ Friday dinner   ☐ Sunday brunch
☐ Out of town guest list, page 45

R

Name_____

Address_____

Phone_____

Email_____

☐ Invitation sent, date_____

Gift_____

_____

_____

☐ Thank you, date_____

☐ Reception   ____ Adults
              ____ Children

Table Seating_____ ☐
_____ ☐
_____ ☐
_____ ☐
_____ ☐
_____ ☐
_____ ☐

☐ Friday dinner   ☐ Sunday brunch
☐ Out of town guest list, page 45

Name _____

_____

Address _____

_____

Phone _____

_____

Email _____

☐ Invitation sent, date _____

Gift _____

_____

_____

☐ Thank you, date _____

☐ Reception _____ Adults
_____ Children

Table Seating _____ ☐

_____ ☐

_____ ☐

_____ ☐

_____ ☐

_____ ☐

_____ ☐

☐ Friday dinner   ☐ Sunday brunch

☐ Out of town guest list, page 45

Name _____

_____

Address _____

_____

Phone _____

_____

Email _____

☐ Invitation sent, date _____

Gift _____

_____

_____

☐ Thank you, date _____

☐ Reception _____ Adults
_____ Children

Table Seating _____ ☐

_____ ☐

_____ ☐

_____ ☐

_____ ☐

_____ ☐

_____ ☐

☐ Friday dinner   ☐ Sunday brunch

☐ Out of town guest list, page 45

Name _____

_____

Address _____

_____

Phone _____

_____

Email _____

☐ Invitation sent, date _____

Gift _____

_____

_____

☐ Thank you, date _____

☐ Reception _____ Adults
_____ Children

Table Seating _____ ☐

_____ ☐

_____ ☐

_____ ☐

_____ ☐

_____ ☐

_____ ☐

☐ Friday dinner   ☐ Sunday brunch

☐ Out of town guest list, page 45

Name_____

_____

Address_____

_____

Phone_____

_____

Email_____

☐ Invitation sent, date_____

Gift_____

_____

_____

☐ Thank you, date_____

☐ Reception _____ Adults _____ Children

Table Seating _____ ☐

_____ ☐

_____ ☐

_____ ☐

_____ ☐

_____ ☐

_____ ☐

☐ Friday dinner ☐ Sunday brunch

☐ Out of town guest list, page 45

Name_____

_____

Address_____

_____

Phone_____

_____

Email_____

☐ Invitation sent, date_____

Gift_____

_____

_____

☐ Thank you, date_____

☐ Reception _____ Adults _____ Children

Table Seating _____ ☐

_____ ☐

_____ ☐

_____ ☐

_____ ☐

_____ ☐

_____ ☐

☐ Friday dinner ☐ Sunday brunch

☐ Out of town guest list, page 45

Name_____

_____

Address_____

_____

Phone_____

_____

Email_____

☐ Invitation sent, date_____

Gift_____

_____

_____

☐ Thank you, date_____

☐ Reception _____ Adults _____ Children

Table Seating _____ ☐

_____ ☐

_____ ☐

_____ ☐

_____ ☐

_____ ☐

_____ ☐

S

☐ Friday dinner ☐ Sunday brunch

☐ Out of town guest list, page 45

Name_____

_____

Address_____

_____

Phone_____

_____

Email_____

☐ Invitation sent, date_____

Gift_____

_____

_____

☐ Thank you, date _____

☐ Reception ____ Adults
____ Children

Table Seating _____ ☐

_____ ☐

_____ ☐

_____ ☐

_____ ☐

_____ ☐

_____ ☐

☐ Friday dinner ☐ Sunday brunch

☐ Out of town guest list, page 45

Name_____

_____

Address_____

_____

Phone_____

_____

Email_____

☐ Invitation sent, date_____

Gift_____

_____

_____

☐ Thank you, date _____

☐ Reception ____ Adults
____ Children

Table Seating _____ ☐

_____ ☐

_____ ☐

_____ ☐

_____ ☐

_____ ☐

_____ ☐

☐ Friday dinner ☐ Sunday brunch

☐ Out of town guest list, page 45

Name_____

_____

Address_____

_____

Phone_____

_____

Email_____

☐ Invitation sent, date_____

Gift_____

_____

_____

☐ Thank you, date _____

☐ Reception ____ Adults
____ Children

Table Seating _____ ☐

_____ ☐

_____ ☐

_____ ☐

_____ ☐

_____ ☐

☐ Friday dinner ☐ Sunday brunch

☐ Out of town guest list, page 45

Name_____

Address_____

_____

Phone_____

_____

Email_____

☐ Invitation sent, date_____

Gift_____

_____

_____

☐ Thank you, date _____

☐ Reception　____ Adults
　　　　　　　____ Children

Table Seating _____ ☐

_____ ☐

_____ ☐

_____ ☐

_____ ☐

_____ ☐

_____ ☐

☐ Friday dinner　☐ Sunday brunch

☐ Out of town guest list, page 45

Name_____

Address_____

_____

Phone_____

_____

Email_____

☐ Invitation sent, date_____

Gift_____

_____

_____

☐ Thank you, date _____

☐ Reception　____ Adults
　　　　　　　____ Children

Table Seating _____ ☐

_____ ☐

_____ ☐

_____ ☐

_____ ☐

_____ ☐

_____ ☐

☐ Friday dinner　☐ Sunday brunch

☐ Out of town guest list, page 45

Name_____

Address_____

_____

Phone_____

_____

Email_____

☐ Invitation sent, date_____

Gift_____

_____

_____

☐ Thank you, date _____

☐ Reception　____ Adults
　　　　　　　____ Children

Table Seating _____ ☐

_____ ☐

_____ ☐

_____ ☐

_____ ☐

_____ ☐

_____ ☐

☐ Friday dinner　☐ Sunday brunch

☐ Out of town guest list, page 45

T

Name_____

_____

Address_____

Phone_____

_____

Email_____

☐ Invitation sent, date_____

Gift_____

_____

_____

☐ Thank you, date _____

☐ Reception   ____ Adults
                  ____ Children

Table Seating _____ ☐

_____ ☐

_____ ☐

_____ ☐

_____ ☐

_____ ☐

_____ ☐

☐ Friday dinner   ☐ Sunday brunch

☐ Out of town guest list, page 45

Name_____

_____

Address_____

Phone_____

_____

Email_____

☐ Invitation sent, date_____

Gift_____

_____

_____

☐ Thank you, date _____

☐ Reception   ____ Adults
                  ____ Children

Table Seating _____ ☐

_____ ☐

_____ ☐

_____ ☐

_____ ☐

_____ ☐

_____ ☐

☐ Friday dinner   ☐ Sunday brunch

☐ Out of town guest list, page 45

Name_____

_____

Address_____

Phone_____

_____

Email_____

☐ Invitation sent, date_____

Gift_____

_____

_____

☐ Thank you, date _____

☐ Reception   ____ Adults
                  ____ Children

Table Seating _____ ☐

_____ ☐

_____ ☐

_____ ☐

_____ ☐

_____ ☐

_____ ☐

☐ Friday dinner   ☐ Sunday brunch

☐ Out of town guest list, page 45

Name _____

Address _____

_____

Phone _____

_____

Email _____

☐ Invitation sent, date _____

Gift _____

_____

_____

☐ Thank you, date _____

☐ Reception   ____ Adults
                 ____ Children

Table Seating _____ ☐

_____ ☐

_____ ☐

_____ ☐

_____ ☐

_____ ☐

_____ ☐

☐ Friday dinner   ☐ Sunday brunch

☐ Out of town guest list, page 45

Name _____

Address _____

_____

Phone _____

_____

Email _____

☐ Invitation sent, date _____

Gift _____

_____

_____

☐ Thank you, date _____

☐ Reception   ____ Adults
                 ____ Children

Table Seating _____ ☐

_____ ☐

_____ ☐

_____ ☐

_____ ☐

_____ ☐

_____ ☐

☐ Friday dinner   ☐ Sunday brunch

☐ Out of town guest list, page 45

Name _____

Address _____

_____

Phone _____

_____

Email _____

☐ Invitation sent, date _____

Gift _____

_____

_____

☐ Thank you, date _____

☐ Reception   ____ Adults
                 ____ Children

Table Seating _____ ☐

_____ ☐

_____ ☐

_____ ☐

_____ ☐

_____ ☐

_____ ☐

☐ Friday dinner   ☐ Sunday brunch

☐ Out of town guest list, page 45

U

Name_____

_____

Address_____

_____

Phone_____

_____

Email_____

☐ Invitation sent, date_____

Gift_____

_____

_____

☐ Thank you, date _____

☐ Reception   _____ Adults
                _____ Children

Table Seating _____ ☐

_____ ☐

_____ ☐

_____ ☐

_____ ☐

_____ ☐

_____ ☐

☐ Friday dinner   ☐ Sunday brunch

☐ Out of town guest list, page 45

Name_____

_____

Address_____

_____

Phone_____

_____

Email_____

☐ Invitation sent, date_____

Gift_____

_____

_____

☐ Thank you, date _____

☐ Reception   _____ Adults
                _____ Children

Table Seating _____ ☐

_____ ☐

_____ ☐

_____ ☐

_____ ☐

_____ ☐

_____ ☐

☐ Friday dinner   ☐ Sunday brunch

☐ Out of town guest list, page 45

Name_____

_____

Address_____

_____

Phone_____

_____

Email_____

☐ Invitation sent, date_____

Gift_____

_____

_____

☐ Thank you, date _____

☐ Reception   _____ Adults
                _____ Children

Table Seating _____ ☐

_____ ☐

_____ ☐

_____ ☐

_____ ☐

_____ ☐

_____ ☐

☐ Friday dinner   ☐ Sunday brunch

☐ Out of town guest list, page 45

Name_____

_____

Address_____

_____

Phone_____

_____

Email_____

☐ Invitation sent, date_____

Gift_____

_____

_____

☐ Thank you, date _____

☐ Reception ____ Adults ____ Children

Table Seating _____ ☐

_____ ☐

_____ ☐

_____ ☐

_____ ☐

_____ ☐

_____ ☐

☐ Friday dinner ☐ Sunday brunch

☐ Out of town guest list, page 45

Name_____

_____

Address_____

_____

Phone_____

_____

Email_____

☐ Invitation sent, date_____

Gift_____

_____

_____

☐ Thank you, date _____

☐ Reception ____ Adults ____ Children

Table Seating _____ ☐

_____ ☐

_____ ☐

_____ ☐

_____ ☐

_____ ☐

_____ ☐

☐ Friday dinner ☐ Sunday brunch

☐ Out of town guest list, page 45

Name_____

_____

Address_____

_____

Phone_____

_____

Email_____

☐ Invitation sent, date_____

Gift_____

_____

_____

☐ Thank you, date _____

☐ Reception ____ Adults ____ Children

Table Seating _____ ☐

_____ ☐

_____ ☐

_____ ☐

_____ ☐

_____ ☐

_____ ☐

☐ Friday dinner ☐ Sunday brunch

☐ Out of town guest list, page 45

V

Name_____

_____

Address_____

_____

Phone_____

_____

Email_____

☐ Invitation sent, date_____

Gift_____

_____

_____

☐ Thank you, date _____

☐ Reception   _____ Adults   _____ Children

Table Seating _____ ☐

_____ ☐

_____ ☐

_____ ☐

_____ ☐

_____ ☐

_____ ☐

☐ Friday dinner   ☐ Sunday brunch

☐ Out of town guest list, page 45

Name_____

_____

Address_____

_____

Phone_____

_____

Email_____

☐ Invitation sent, date_____

Gift_____

_____

_____

☐ Thank you, date _____

☐ Reception   _____ Adults   _____ Children

Table Seating _____ ☐

_____ ☐

_____ ☐

_____ ☐

_____ ☐

_____ ☐

_____ ☐

☐ Friday dinner   ☐ Sunday brunch

☐ Out of town guest list, page 45

Name_____

_____

Address_____

_____

Phone_____

_____

Email_____

☐ Invitation sent, date_____

Gift_____

_____

_____

☐ Thank you, date _____

☐ Reception   _____ Adults   _____ Children

Table Seating _____ ☐

_____ ☐

_____ ☐

_____ ☐

_____ ☐

_____ ☐

_____ ☐

☐ Friday dinner   ☐ Sunday brunch

☐ Out of town guest list, page 45

Name_____

_____

Address_____

_____

Phone_____

_____

Email_____

☐ Invitation sent, date_____

Gift_____

_____

_____

☐ Thank you, date_____

☐ Reception   ____ Adults
____ Children

Table Seating _____ ☐

_____ ☐

_____ ☐

_____ ☐

_____ ☐

_____ ☐

_____ ☐

☐ Friday dinner   ☐ Sunday brunch

☐ Out of town guest list, page 45

Name_____

_____

Address_____

_____

Phone_____

_____

Email_____

☐ Invitation sent, date_____

Gift_____

_____

_____

☐ Thank you, date_____

☐ Reception   ____ Adults
____ Children

Table Seating _____ ☐

_____ ☐

_____ ☐

_____ ☐

_____ ☐

_____ ☐

_____ ☐

☐ Friday dinner   ☐ Sunday brunch

☐ Out of town guest list, page 45

Name_____

_____

Address_____

_____

Phone_____

_____

Email_____

☐ Invitation sent, date_____

Gift_____

_____

_____

☐ Thank you, date_____

☐ Reception   ____ Adults
____ Children

Table Seating _____ ☐

_____ ☐

_____ ☐

_____ ☐

_____ ☐

_____ ☐

_____ ☐

☐ Friday dinner   ☐ Sunday brunch

☐ Out of town guest list, page 45

W

Name_____

_____

Address_____

_____

Phone_____

_____

Email_____

☐ Invitation sent, date_____

Gift_____

_____

_____

☐ Thank you, date _____

☐ Reception   _____ Adults
               _____ Children

Table Seating _____ ☐

_____ ☐

_____ ☐

_____ ☐

_____ ☐

_____ ☐

_____ ☐

☐ Friday dinner   ☐ Sunday brunch

☐ Out of town guest list, page 45

Name_____

_____

Address_____

_____

Phone_____

_____

Email_____

☐ Invitation sent, date_____

Gift_____

_____

_____

☐ Thank you, date _____

☐ Reception   _____ Adults
               _____ Children

Table Seating _____ ☐

_____ ☐

_____ ☐

_____ ☐

_____ ☐

_____ ☐

_____ ☐

☐ Friday dinner   ☐ Sunday brunch

☐ Out of town guest list, page 45

Name_____

_____

Address_____

_____

Phone_____

_____

Email_____

☐ Invitation sent, date_____

Gift_____

_____

_____

☐ Thank you, date _____

☐ Reception   _____ Adults
               _____ Children

Table Seating _____ ☐

_____ ☐

_____ ☐

_____ ☐

_____ ☐

_____ ☐

_____ ☐

☐ Friday dinner   ☐ Sunday brunch

☐ Out of town guest list, page 45

Name_____

Address_____

_____

Phone_____

_____

Email_____

☐ Invitation sent, date_____

Gift_____

_____

_____

☐ Thank you, date_____

☐ Reception   _____ Adults
               _____ Children

Table Seating_____   ☐

_____   ☐

_____   ☐

_____   ☐

_____   ☐

_____   ☐

_____   ☐

☐ Friday dinner   ☐ Sunday brunch

☐ Out of town guest list, page 45

Name_____

Address_____

_____

Phone_____

_____

Email_____

☐ Invitation sent, date_____

Gift_____

_____

_____

☐ Thank you, date_____

☐ Reception   _____ Adults
               _____ Children

Table Seating_____   ☐

_____   ☐

_____   ☐

_____   ☐

_____   ☐

_____   ☐

_____   ☐

☐ Friday dinner   ☐ Sunday brunch

☐ Out of town guest list, page 45

Name_____

Address_____

_____

Phone_____

_____

Email_____

☐ Invitation sent, date_____

Gift_____

_____

_____

☐ Thank you, date_____

☐ Reception   _____ Adults
               _____ Children

Table Seating_____   ☐

_____   ☐

_____   ☐

_____   ☐

_____   ☐

_____   ☐

_____   ☐

☐ Friday dinner   ☐ Sunday brunch

☐ Out of town guest list, page 45

X

Name_____

_____

Address_____

_____

Phone_____

_____

Email_____

☐ Invitation sent, date_____

Gift_____

_____

_____

☐ Thank you, date_____

☐ Reception _____ Adults
             _____ Children

Table Seating _____ ☐

_____ ☐

_____ ☐

_____ ☐

_____ ☐

_____ ☐

_____ ☐

_____ ☐

☐ Friday dinner   ☐ Sunday brunch

☐ Out of town guest list, page 45

Name_____

_____

Address_____

_____

Phone_____

_____

Email_____

☐ Invitation sent, date_____

Gift_____

_____

_____

☐ Thank you, date_____

☐ Reception _____ Adults
             _____ Children

Table Seating _____ ☐

_____ ☐

_____ ☐

_____ ☐

_____ ☐

_____ ☐

☐ Friday dinner   ☐ Sunday brunch

☐ Out of town guest list, page 45

Name_____

_____

Address_____

_____

Phone_____

_____

Email_____

☐ Invitation sent, date_____

Gift_____

_____

_____

☐ Thank you, date_____

☐ Reception _____ Adults
             _____ Children

Table Seating _____ ☐

_____ ☐

_____ ☐

_____ ☐

_____ ☐

_____ ☐

☐ Friday dinner   ☐ Sunday brunch

☐ Out of town guest list, page 45

Name_____

Address_____

_____

Phone_____

_____

Email_____

☐ Invitation sent, date_____

Gift_____

_____

_____

☐ Thank you, date_____

☐ Reception   _____ Adults   _____ Children

Table Seating _____ ☐

_____ ☐

_____ ☐

_____ ☐

_____ ☐

_____ ☐

_____ ☐

☐ Friday dinner   ☐ Sunday brunch

☐ Out of town guest list, page 45

Name_____

_____

Address_____

_____

Phone_____

_____

Email_____

☐ Invitation sent, date_____

Gift_____

_____

_____

☐ Thank you, date_____

☐ Reception   _____ Adults   _____ Children

Table Seating _____ ☐

_____ ☐

_____ ☐

_____ ☐

_____ ☐

_____ ☐

_____ ☐

☐ Friday dinner   ☐ Sunday brunch

☐ Out of town guest list, page 45

Name_____

Address_____

_____

Phone_____

_____

Email_____

☐ Invitation sent, date_____

Gift_____

_____

_____

☐ Thank you, date_____

☐ Reception   _____ Adults   _____ Children

Table Seating _____ ☐

_____ ☐

_____ ☐

_____ ☐

_____ ☐

_____ ☐

_____ ☐

☐ Friday dinner   ☐ Sunday brunch

☐ Out of town guest list, page 45

Y

Name_____

Address_____

_____

Phone_____

_____

Email_____

☐ Invitation sent, date_____

Gift_____

_____

_____

☐ Thank you, date _____

☐ Reception   ____ Adults
                              ____ Children
Table Seating _____ ☐
_____ ☐
_____ ☐
_____ ☐
_____ ☐
_____ ☐
_____ ☐

☐ Friday dinner   ☐ Sunday brunch
☐ Out of town guest list, page 45

Name_____

Address_____

_____

Phone_____

_____

Email_____

☐ Invitation sent, date_____

Gift_____

_____

_____

☐ Thank you, date _____

☐ Reception   ____ Adults
                              ____ Children
Table Seating _____ ☐
_____ ☐
_____ ☐
_____ ☐
_____ ☐
_____ ☐
_____ ☐

☐ Friday dinner   ☐ Sunday brunch
☐ Out of town guest list, page 45

Name_____

Address_____

_____

Phone_____

_____

Email_____

☐ Invitation sent, date_____

Gift_____

_____

_____

☐ Thank you, date _____

☐ Reception   ____ Adults
                              ____ Children
Table Seating _____ ☐
_____ ☐
_____ ☐
_____ ☐
_____ ☐
_____ ☐
_____ ☐

☐ Friday dinner   ☐ Sunday brunch
☐ Out of town guest list, page 45

Name

Address

Phone

Email

☐ Invitation sent, date

Gift

☐ Thank you, date

☐ Reception
_____ Adults
_____ Children

Table Seating _____ ☐
_____ ☐
_____ ☐
_____ ☐
_____ ☐
_____ ☐

☐ Friday dinner   ☐ Sunday brunch
☐ Out of town guest list, page 45

Name

Address

Phone

Email

☐ Invitation sent, date

Gift

☐ Thank you, date

☐ Reception
_____ Adults
_____ Children

Table Seating _____ ☐
_____ ☐
_____ ☐
_____ ☐
_____ ☐
_____ ☐

☐ Friday dinner   ☐ Sunday brunch
☐ Out of town guest list, page 45

Name

Address

Phone

Email

☐ Invitation sent, date

Gift

☐ Thank you, date

☐ Reception
_____ Adults
_____ Children

Table Seating _____ ☐
_____ ☐
_____ ☐
_____ ☐
_____ ☐
_____ ☐

☐ Friday dinner   ☐ Sunday brunch
☐ Out of town guest list, page 45

Z

GUEST	NUMBER ATTENDING							
	FRIDAY			SATURDAY			SUNDAY	
	DINNER		Oneg	RECEPTION		Kid-dush	BRUNCH	
	ADULT	CHILD		ADULT	CHILD		ADULT	CHILD

GUEST	NUMBER ATTENDING							
	FRIDAY			SATURDAY			SUNDAY	
	DINNER		Oneg	RECEPTION		Kid-dush	BRUNCH	
	ADULT	CHILD		ADULT	CHILD		ADULT	CHILD

GUEST	NUMBER ATTENDING							
	FRIDAY			SATURDAY			SUNDAY	
	DINNER		Oneg	RECEPTION		Kid-dush	BRUNCH	
	ADULT	CHILD		ADULT	CHILD		ADULT	CHILD

GUEST	NUMBER ATTENDING							
	FRIDAY			SATURDAY			SUNDAY	
	DINNER		Oneg	RECEPTION		Kid-dush	BRUNCH	
	ADULT	CHILD		ADULT	CHILD		ADULT	CHILD

GUEST	NUMBER ATTENDING							
	FRIDAY			SATURDAY			SUNDAY	
	DINNER		Oneg	RECEPTION		Kid-dush	BRUNCH	
	ADULT	CHILD		ADULT	CHILD		ADULT	CHILD

GUEST	NUMBER ATTENDING							
	FRIDAY			SATURDAY			SUNDAY	
	DINNER		Oneg	RECEPTION		Kid-dush	BRUNCH	
	ADULT	CHILD		ADULT	CHILD		ADULT	CHILD